D1371475

SEPT '01

From the Nation's #1 Educational Publisher K-12

The McGraw·Hill
JUNIOR ACADEMIC SERIES

My First PICTURE WORD BOOK

Starring the Looney Tunes!

Written by Robert Schechter

Cover Illustration by Animated Arts!™ and Allen Helbig

Interior Illustration by Duendes del Sur

This book is dedicated to our children –
Alyx, Nathan, Fred S., Dawn, Rashaun, Brianna, Michele, Bradley, BriAnne, Kristie,
Sydney, Caroline, Dominic, Corey, Lindsey, Spencer, Morgan, Brooke, Cody, Emily, Phillip,
August, Julianna, Gwen, Daniel, Miller, Ashley – and to all children
who deserve a good education and who love to learn.

McGraw-Hill Consumer Products & Warner Bros.

Credits:
McGraw-Hill Consumer Products Editorial/Production Team
Vincent F. Douglas, B.S. and M. Ed.
Tracey E. Dils
Tracy R. Paulus
Jennifer Blashkiw Pawley

Warner Bros. Worldwide Publishing
Editorial/Production Team
Michael Harkavy   Charles Carney
Paula Allen   Allen Helbig
Victoria Selover   Robert Schechter

Design Studio
Cover: McGraw-Hill Consumer Products/Warner Bros.
Interior: Stuart & Stuart

Illustrators
Cover: Animated Arts!™/Allen Helbig
Interior: Duendes del Sur

McGraw-Hill
Consumer Products
*A Division of The **McGraw·Hill** Companies*

Send all inquiries to:
McGraw-Hill Consumer Products
8787 Orion Place
Columbus, Ohio 43240-4027

Hard Cover Edition: 1-57768-205-X
Soft Cover Edition: 1-57768-206-8

1 2 3 4 5 6 7 8 9 10 RRW 04 03 02 01 00 99

TABLE OF CONTENTS

LOONEY TUNES LETTERS

Directions: Look at each of the letters of the alphabet and the pictures that go with them. Can you name the three things in each picture that begin with the letter shown? (The letters Xx and Zz have only two things.) Some of the words are names of the Looney Tunes characters.

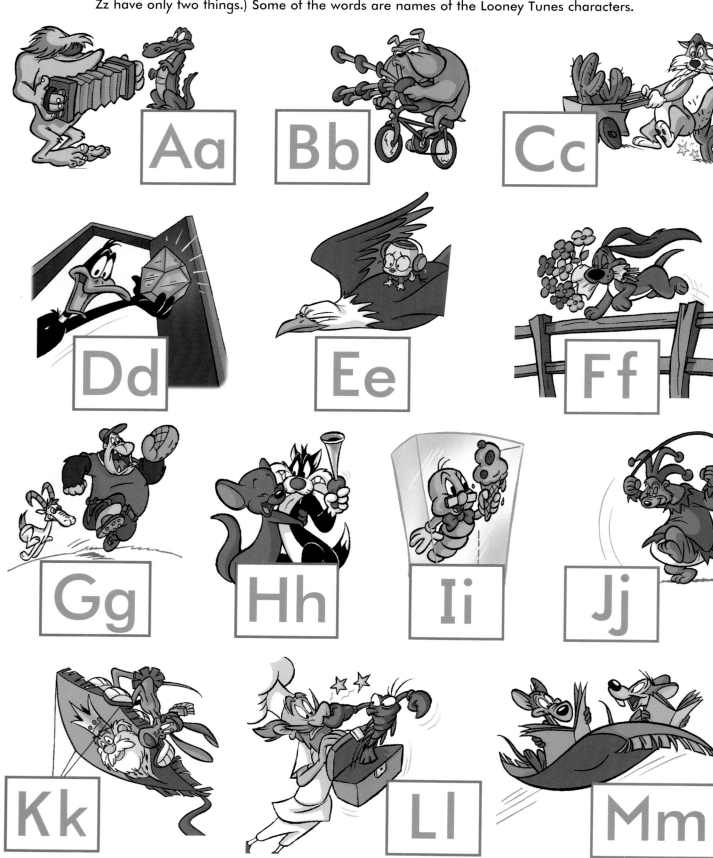

Nn

Oo

Pp

Qq

Rr

Ss

Tt

Uu

Vv

Ww

Xx

Yy

Zz

See page 64 for answers.

NUMBERS ARE LOONEY, TOO!

In each picture below, count the objects that are the same from 1 to 10.

Find the numbers 11-20 in the pictures below.

MISS CALCULUS'S STUDIO SCHOOL

GREEN
YELLOW

"**L**esson time, students," says Miss Calculus. But the students don't want to study. There's too much to touch, break, and spill. *They're quiet,* Miss Calculus thinks. *I wonder where they went.*

triangle

red

yellow

diamond

square

orange

School is for WISE GUYS!

purple

star

oval

brown

circle

pink

blue

heart

green

rectangle

white

black

MUSCULAR BEACH

IT'S NOT TOUGH TO LOOK BUFF!

Even Looney Tunes like to stay in shape. But stretch, sweat, churn, and burn? Not when there's Muscular Beach — where a tight tummy, shapely shoulders, and big muscles are just a picture away.

back

neck

hand

mouth

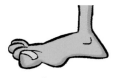

foot

chin

leg

knee

chest

cheek

stomach

shoulder

finger

hair

nose

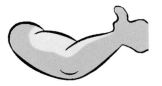
arm

ear

eye

1

THE GLOOM AND DOOM COSTUME BALL

Witch Hazel is invited to the Mad Scientist's costume party.

"Shred of rag
Scrap of plaid
Give us clothes
That look plain bad!"

POOF!!! "AAAAAAAAHHH!!!!!!!!" she screams at the ugly, awful, terrible... FASHIONABLE clothes. "These outfits are so nasty-looking, we'll win best costume for sure!"

belt

vest

shoes

dress

T-shirt

shorts

2

button

sweater

bow tie

sneakers

turtleneck

blue jeans

zipper

skirt

shirt

pants

socks

tie

A CAT NAPS

Some say, "When the cat's away, the mice will play." But when Claude Cat falls asleep, the mice rock and roll without a peep. When Claude wakes up, the mice will scatter, telling him to "Have a <u>mice</u> day!"

bed

lamp

quilt

pillow

window

blanket

 bookshelf

 telephone

 closet

 mirror

 hanger

 curtains

 dresser

 computer

 light switch

 night stand

 teddy bear

 alarm clock

BATH TO GLORY

The Giant's birthday party is tonight. Although he can see over the highest mountain and lift a mighty oak tree, he still needs help to wash his back. "SCRUB A LITTLE HIGHER! AND WHO IS MAKING NOISE?" he roars. "RUBBER DUCKY NEEDS HIS NAP!"

sink

soap

comb

brush

towel

sponge

 mirror

 toilet

 shower

bathtub

 shampoo

 tissues

 hair dryer

toilet paper

 toothpaste

 toothbrush

 rubber duck

medicine cabinet

Every duck dreams of going to Mars. "Speak for yourself," screams Daffy as Martians mistake him for the famous *Duck Dodgers*. See, for a duck, Daffy's a real chicken. When a "Duck Dodgers" cartoon comes on TV, the Martians run away . "Some days a duck can't win," Daffy says.

rug

lamp

VCR

clock

door

couch

pillow

footstool

armchair

light bulb

candle

picture

fireplace

television

stereo

bookcase

telephone

vacuum cleaner

19

TOO MANY CHEFS
(BUT NONE WHO CAN COOK)

Welcome to Pasquale's Restaurant, where the customers are hungry and the chefs are helpless and clumsy. And they are not very good cooks. After putting out fires and stopping floods, Pasquale serves a meal you can never forget, or eat.

oven

stove

bowl

glass

sink

table

plate

faucet

dishwasher

silverware

napkin

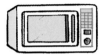

microwave

cupboard

refrigerator

toaster

garbage can

tablecloth

pot

GOPHER THE GOLD

Elmer Fudd has a green thumb. He also has brown gophers ruining his garden. "Dose wittle wascals," he yells. His voice echoes under the pail. Elmer thought gardening would be quiet and peaceful. "I'd wather be hunting wabbits!" he decides.

bee

bird

soil

ants

pail

nest

tree

snail

birdhouse

flowerpot

rake

flowers

wheelbarrow

butterfly

grass

trowel

garden hose

watering can

A VISIT TO YOSEMITE (SAM'S)

Yosemite Sam's
Park
Grown-Up Day

What in tarnation??? It's *Grown-Up Day* at Yosemite Sam's Park. That means children-at-heart can ride, swing, and play. How do the kids like *Grown-Up Day*? It's hard to say. None of them can find any room left in the park.

kite

slide

bench

tree

grass

seesaw

4

bird

fence

sandbox

swing set

statue

children

roller blades

baby carriage

tricycle

fountain

monkey bars

merry-go-round

GO TO MARKET

Being wacky really makes you hungry. What gives Road Runner his get-up and BEEP? What breakfast food keeps Gruesome Gorilla gruesome? For these and other eating tips, head for Acme Market, where the Looney Tunes stop, shop, and swap double coupons.

eggs

milk

fish

money

bread

butter

 fruits

 cereal

 vegetables

 cash register

 cheese

 coupons

 butcher

 canned food

 scale

 cashier

 basket

 shopping cart

STAR WRECKS

Come to "Star Wrecks" where looney stars buy broken cars. Need a beat-up jeep cheap? A crashed train? A smashed plane? Prices are lower than the tires on our taxicab. And our doors are open 24 hours, because they are too dented to close!

bus

boat

taxi

jeep

car

train

truck

bicycle

skateboard

fire truck

wagon

school bus

motorcycle

in-line skates

airplane

balloon

convertible

station wagon

LIFE IN THE BIG CITY

The Looney Tunes artists have made a big mistake. They put country toons in the city, and city folks on a farm. Next thing you know, they'll put Marvin The Martian on Earth, and blast Elmer Fudd to Mars. Okay, maybe they <u>do</u> know what they're doing!

pig

hay

taxi

traffic light

newsstand

bus

30

horse

cow

hen

parking meter

sheep

rooster

skyscraper

barn

tractor

bus stop

restaurant

telephone booth

FINDER OF LOST PETS

In the Old West, some sheriffs captured bad guys, and others were "Finders of Lost Pets." Did your doggie disappear? Did your guppie go bye-bye? Did your froggie flee? The Sheriff can find anything, except the keys to the pet cage. Oops!

cat

bone

dog

aquarium

rabbit

snake

 puppy

 kitten

 turtle

 doghouse

 horse

 lizard

 hamster

 parrot

 leash

 frog

 goldfish

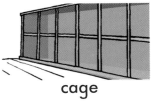 cage

PLEASE DON'T FEED THE MARTIANS

MARS ZOO

OPEN

Marvin The Martian and K-9 love their jobs at the Mars Zoo. During the day, visitors watch as Marvin and K-9 teach the Earth animals to play Martian games. But when the zoo closes, the Earth creatures trade places with Marvin and his friends and teach them how to play Earth games.

seal

deer

bear

panda

lion

camel

MARS ZOO

CLOSED

zebra

penguin

gorilla

alligator

tiger

vulture

giraffe

hippopotamus

monkey

leopard

elephant

rhinoceros

STOP! IN THE NAME OF TOYS

Crime really doesn't pay. Just ask Rocky and Mugsy, two bad guys who were bowled over and tied up by a kid's best friend – toys. So be nice to your playthings. The game you save may be your own.

top

kite

ball

cards

doll

jack-in-the-box

train

blocks

crayon

jump rope

robot

dominos

marbles

rocking horse

puppet

puzzle

soldiers

teddy bear

A REAL CLASS ACT!

The Looney Tunes are a riot. No, really, they are an out-of-control riot! Fur and feathers fly fast and furious. Then Granny calls Acme Kennel. "Come and get my students," she says. UH-OH!!! Soon, the animals will sit sweetly, and Granny will be back in charge completely.

desk

book

flag

globe

chair

paper

chalk

ruler

scissors

paintbrush

clock

eraser

teacher

chalkboard

paint

pencil

students

pencil sharpener

BEACH BLANKET BORING

Professor Calculus went to the beach last summer. He took lots of pictures. Only one picture came out okay. The others got wet. But he likes to show them to his wife anyway. Get ready for a long, LONG night. The slide show has begun!

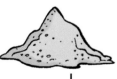

sand

ball

crab

wave

pail

beach

ocean

sandals

starfish

sunglasses

shark

seaweed

seashell

umbrella

clams

shovel

lighthouse

bathing suit

The Abominable Snowman loves the winter. The summer sun burns his fur. In the spring, the new flowers make him sneeze. And no one likes sweeping leaves in the fall. But in the winter he builds "Abominable Snowpeople" so that he can have friends who aren't afraid of him.

sun

hat

bird

snow

sled

nest

tree

acorn

flower

squirrel

scarf

shorts

leaves

snowman

cloud

T-shirt

pumpkin

sunglasses

WHAT MAKES CASBAH RUN?

Casbah Rabbit thinks he is a super athlete. He scores in basketball, baseball, soccer, and tennis. In fact, he is a hero, until he wakes up. "Does anybody need a clean towel?"

net

ice skates

skis

helmet

baseball

football

golf ball

volleyball

baseball bat

hockey stick

ski poles

basketball

soccer ball

baseball glove

golf club

hockey puck

tennis ball

tennis racket

SILLY SLEEP SONGS

Some nights, Junyer Bear has trouble sleeping. It is a good thing Papa Bear keeps an orchestra around. Sometimes, a lullaby is better than counting sheep. Tomorrow night, Junyer will be at Grandma's house. He'll pack light — a drum set, or maybe some horns.

tuba

piano

harp

flute

drums

bugle

guitar

trumpet

harmonica

saxophone

violin

accordion

trombone

xylophone

cymbals

recorder

triangle

tambourine

THE MIGHTY ANGELO'S FLEA-RING CIRCUS

The flea circus appearing on Sam the sheep dog is the greatest show on fur. Cootie the Clown has traveled all over the world, performing on French poodles, Irish setters, Great Danes, and even a German shepherd. What does Sam say about all this? He says, "Woof."

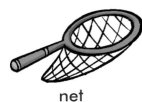
net

tent

cage

lion

ring

whip

clown

acrobat

juggler

balloon

horse

popcorn

trapeze

ringmaster

ladder

elephant

tightrope

lion tamer

THE TUNE-UP

It's time for Mechanical Rabbit's tune-up. Doctor Mad Scientist and his staff chop, hammer, saw, sand, and wrench away any problems. Some fresh bolts and a pretty paint job, and Mechanical Rabbit is as good as new.

saw

tacks

ax

board

nails

ruler

drill

hammer

toolbox

workbench

paint

pliers

sawhorse

paintbrush

screws

wrench

sandpaper

screwdriver

5

Once upon a time, The Giant was thin. Then he discovered "All-You-Can-Eat" restaurants. His weight went up, up, up, and twelve restaurants went out of business. Francois and Louis must hurry and close before The Giant eats them out of food, drink, and jobs.

peas

milk

corn

apple

cake

pizza

bread

banana

popcorn

watermelon

cheese

grapes

carrot

orange juice

muffin

tomato

pancakes

ice cream cone

53

PICNIC IN THE AIR

Ants came from far and near. Not many, just a few million to attack Witch Hazel's picnic feast. But wait, no fair! The food is flying away. Luckily, Elmer Fudd's food can't fly. It stays on the ground — fresh, tasty, and ready for ants.

pie

hot dog

fly

pickle

ants

cooler

basket

plate

chicken

sandwich

grill

blanket

napkin

hamburger

ketchup

cookies

mustard

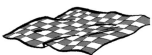
silverware

LOONEY TUNES OPPOSITES OLYMPICS

At the Looney Tunes Opposites Olympics, short winners feel tall and tall losers are knocked down to size. There is joy and sadness, smiles and tears, Porky and Petunia. So, what is the opposite of Looney Tunes? Something dull, don't you think?

big

little

dirty

clean

thick

thin

few

many

front

back

short   tall

young

old

top

bottom

happy

sad

OH, AND BY THE WAY...

"**Y**ou'll notice that the people who made this book didn't notice that yours truly here got himself into every scene except one! Not bad, huh?

Did I do it for fame? Nope. Carrots? No. To make Daffy Duck jealous? Mmmmmmmm… could be!

See if you can find me in each scene. I could be in a crowd, or on the face of a wristwatch. Can you count how many times I snuck into the picture?

Oh, and by the way – there's one picture that I didn't get in. Here's a hint: You'll feel CRABBY if you don't find this picture, but you won't be BORED.

Okay – you can start searchin' now. It'll be fun, take my word for it."

(See page 64 for answer.)

WORD LIST

Aa

accordion 47
acorn 43
acrobat 49
airplane 29
alarm clock 15
alligator 35
ants 22, 54
apple 52
aquarium 32
arm 11
armchair 19
ax 50

Bb

baby carriage 25
back 10, 57
ball 36, 40
balloon 29, 49
banana 53

barn 31
baseball 44
baseball bat 45
baseball glove 45
basket 27, 55
basketball 45
bathing suit 41
bathtub 17
beach 40
bear 34
bed 14
bee 22
belt 12
bench 24
bicycle 29
big 56
bird 22, 25, 42
birdhouse 23
black 9
blanket 14, 55
blocks 37
blue 9
blue jeans 13
board 50
boat 28
bone 32
book 38
bookcase 19
bookshelf 15
bottom 57
bow tie 13

bowl 20
bread 26, 53
brown 9
brush 16
bugle 46
bus 28, 30
bus stop 31
butcher 27
butter 26
butterfly 23
button 13

Cc

cage 33, 48
cake 52
camel 34
candle 19
canned food 27
car 28
cards 36
carrot 53
cash register 27
cashier 27
cat 32
cereal 27
chair 38
chalk 39
chalkboard 39
cheek 11
cheese 27, 53
chest 11
chicken 55
children 25
chin 10

59

Tt

Uu

Vv

Ww

Xx

Yy

Zz

ANSWER KEY:

PAGES 4-5

Aa – Abominable Snowman, accordion, alligator
Bb – Butch Bulldog, bagpipes, bicycle
Cc – Claude Cat, cactus, cart
Dd – Daffy Duck, diamond, door
Ee – Eggbert, earmuffs, eagle
Ff – Frisky Puppy, fence, flowers
Gg – Gabby Goat, gorilla, glove
Hh – Hippity Hopper, hug, horn
Ii – Inchworm, ice cube, ice cream cone
Jj – Junyer Bear, jump rope, jester
Kk – K-9, kite, king
Ll – (Chef) Louis, lunchbox, lobster
Mm – mice, magic carpet, magazines
Nn – Nelly the Giraffe, napkin, newspaper

Oo – Oliver Owl, oranges, octopus
Pp – Porky Pig, piano, pigeon
Qq – Quentin Quail, quarter, question mark
Rr – Road Runner, road, radio
Ss – Speedy Gonzalez, shower, soap
Tt – Taz, television, trumpet
Uu – umpire, unicycle, umbrella
Vv – vulture, vest, violin
Ww – (Big Bad) Wolf, whale, windmill
Xx – x-ray, xylophone
Yy – Yosemite Sam, yawn, yellow
Zz – zipper, zebra

PAGE 58

Beach Blanket Boring, pages 40-41